My Spelling Workbook

Prim-Ed
Publishing

BRACKNELL FOREST
EDUCATION CENTRE

CW00842763

Prim-Ed Publishing would like to thank the teachers and pupils from the following schools for their assistance in the production of this *My Spelling Workbook* programme:

Merrylee Primary School, Glasgow

Balbardie Primary School, West Lothian

Brackens Primary School, Dundee

Braehead Primary School, Dumbarton

East Fulton Primary School, Renfrewshire

Knockburn Primary School, Glasgow

Pitfour Primary School, Aberdeenshire

Saracen Primary School, Glasgow

St. Catherine's Primary School, Glasgow

The Mary Russell School, Renfrewshire

Woodlands Primary School, Renfrewshire

My Spelling Workbook – Book G
© Prim-Ed Publishing

Offices in: United Kingdom: PO Box 2840, Coventry, CV6 5ZY
Australia: PO Box 332, Greenwood, Western Australia 6924
Republic of Ireland: Bosheen, New Ross, Co. Wexford, Ireland

Published in 2003 Prim-Ed Publishing
ISBN 1 86400 767 2

Introduction

Welcome to *My Spelling Workbook*. This book has lots of different activities to help you improve your spelling. Here are some tips to show you the best way to use your book.

- **Learning Words**

  Each list of words in the book has two practise columns to write the words. There is also a column for your teacher to tick if you get your dictation correct. Any words which you spell wrongly can be added to the 'Difficult Words I Have Found' table. You can also add any difficult words you find.

- **Look, Say, Cover, Write, Check**

  These words are to remind you of the best way to learn to spell. You should follow this when you are learning each word. Use the flap to cover the list words when you practise them.

- **Recording your Scores**

  At the back of the book, you will find a grid for recording your scores for each unit. This will help you to keep track of how you are improving with your spelling.

- **How to Become a Better Speller**

  1. *Have a go!*
     Write the word on the piece of paper.
     Does it look right? If it doesn't look right, try writing it another way.

  2. *Look around your classroom*
     There are probably many words around you that you just didn't notice.

  3. *Use a dictionary*
     Try using a dictionary before you ask a teacher.

  4. *Ask the teacher*
     If you have tried the first three, then ask a teacher for help.

Contents

Revision Unit 1

List Words	Practise	Practise	D
diamond			
idea			
business			
chocolate			
reference			
fulfil			
necessary			
atmosphere			
music			
conscience			

All Mixed Up

1. Unjumble these revision words.

   (a) c h e a t c o o l   _____

   (b) s e s s u b i n   _____

   (c) m a n i o d d   _____

   (d) n i c e s o c c e n   _____

   (e) f e e r c r e e n   _____

   (f) f l u f l i   _____

   (g) e s a n e c s y r   _____

   (h) u s c i m   _____

   (i) t h e s o m a p e r   _____

Shape Sorter

2. Write a word that fits in the shape.

   (a)

   (b)

   (c)

   (d)

Missing Words

3. Complete using the revision words.

   (a) It was _____ to have a good _____ for the job.

   (b) In my spare time I like to listen to _____ and eat _____.

   (c) He saw the _____ but his _____ wouldn't let him take it.

   (d) This hostile _____ is not good for _____!

4. Find 12 mistakes and write them correctly on the lines.

> My idee to help him fullfil his ambition to work in the musik busness, by writing
>
> _____
>
> the nessecar refarence, troubles my conshence Finding the stolen dimond
>
> _____
>
> ring in his choclate has caused a dreaadful atmosfere in the studio.
>
> _____

Word Hunt

5. (a) Which word has only one consonant? _____

(b) Which word contains a smaller word that means 'wrongdoing'?

_____

(c) Which word has four 'e's? _____

Alphabetical Order

6. Write all the revision words in alphabetical order.

_____

_____

_____

Vertical Challenge

7. (a) Write the answers to each clue in the correct place, horizontally on the grid.

- Company   (8)
- A thief should have one!   (10)
- Concept   (4)
- Valuable gem   (7)
- Essential (9)

(b) Write the word in the highlighted vertical column. _____

(c) Write a clue for this word. _____

_____

List Words	Practise	Practise	D
moreover			
consequently			
nonetheless			
since			
whatever			
furthermore			
meanwhile			
therefore			
believe			
received			

All Mixed Up

1. Unjumble the list words.

  (a) w e a v e t h r   _____

  (b) s h e s e n t l o n e _____

  (c) c e e r d i v e   _____

  (d) h e r r o f e e t   _____

  (e) r o h t e m f u e r r _____

  (f) o e v r m r o e   _____

Small Words

2. Write the list word that contains these small words.

  (a) net _____

  (b) hat _____

  (c) lie _____

  (d) her _____

         _____

  (e) sin _____

Mirror Writing

3. Write the mirror written words correctly.

  (a) furthermore _____

  (b) nonetheless _____

  (c) whatever _____

  (d) since _____

  (e) meanwhile _____

Revision Words	
miserable	gigantic
produce	apostrophe
arrow	phobia

Difficult words I have found	Practise	Practise

4. Use list and revision words to solve this crossword.

Across

3. Wretched.
5. In spite of everything.
7. Anything at all.
9. In addition.
10. Manufacture.
12. Have faith in.
13. Pointer.
14. After the event.
15. Was given.

Down

1. In the interim.
2. And as well as that.
4. As a result.
6. Thus.
8. A punctuation mark.
10. Extreme fear.   11. Enormous.

Sentences

5. Write each of these words in a sentence.

(a) phobia _____

_____

(b) miserable _____

_____

Secret Code

6. Use the secret code to find out the list or revision word.

(a) _ _ _ _ _ _ _
2 5 8 7 5 14 5

(b) _ _ _ _ _
13 7 10 3 5

(c) _ _ _ _ _ _ _ _
9 11 12 5 11 14 5 12

(d) _ _ _ _ _ _ _ _ _
9 5 1 10 15 6 7 8 5

(e) _ _ _ _ _ _ _ _
12 5 3 5 7 14 5 4

a	b	c	d	e	h	i	l	m	n	o	r	s	v	w
1	2	3	4	5	6	7	8	9	10	11	12	13	14	15

List Words	Practise	Practise	D
monologue			
monorail			
monopoly			
monotone			
university			
union			
universal			
unisex			
continuous			
industrial			

Jumbled Letters

1. Two list words are jumbled together. Write the two words.

   (a)   poolnoonmyinu

   _____ + _____

   (b)   duxisentaliunirs

   _____ + _____

   (c)   oruvanimnosyieltri

   _____ + _____

Secret Words

2. (a) Change 'momo' to 'dia' in monologue.

   _____

   (b) Change 'al' to 'e' in universal._____

   (c) Change 'al' to 'ous' in industrial._____

Word Challenge

3. Make as many words as you can from letters in this word.

   universal

   _____

   _____

   _____

Revision Words	
require	clique
definitely	mascara
religion	suspend

Difficult words I have found	Practise	Practise

4. Find these list and revision words in the word search.

monologue   university

monopoly   universal

monorail   union

monotone   unisex

continuous   industrial

require   clique

definitely   mascara

religion   suspend

c	q	m	y	l	e	t	i	n	i	f	e	d
l	o	o	u	n	i	v	e	r	s	a	l	w
i	i	n	d	u	s	t	r	i	a	l	c	m
q	s	o	t	y	t	r	e	w	q	a	v	o
u	u	p	l	i	a	r	o	n	o	m	b	n
e	s	o	m	n	n	b	v	c	o	s	o	o
k	p	l	y	u	i	u	r	n	x	i	n	t
l	e	y	t	l	o	e	o	x	n	d	m	o
p	n	l	r	p	q	l	e	u	z	f	p	n
o	d	k	e	u	o	s	w	q	s	g	o	e
i	n	o	i	g	i	l	e	r	j	h	i	e
u	u	r	u	n	i	v	e	r	s	i	t	y
y	e	e	u	t	r	a	r	a	c	s	a	m

Memory Master

5. (a) Cover the list and revision words. Write two from memory.

_____   _____

   (b) For each word, write a question that has the word as its answer.

   (i) _____

   (ii) _____

Mixed Up Sentences

6. Unjumble the sentences.

   (a) delivered continuous a in He monotone. lecture the

   _____

   (b) are His university. good, into will results definitely get he so

   _____

   (c) action conditions. took The company pay for against better the union industrial

   _____

   (d) suspend due the had service to monorail the to snow. They

   _____

   (e) model to we be If will you mascara. a you to require want wear

   _____

List Words	Practise	Practise	D
duel			
duo			
duet			
dual			
bilingual			
biceps			
binary			
bikini			
consequence			
imaginary			

Alphabetical Order

1. Write all of the list words in alphabetical order.

    _____

    _____

    _____

    _____

    _____

    _____

    _____

    _____

Revision Words

emphasis

persuade

quit

jewellery

allergy

project

Extend Yourself

2. The prefix 'bi' means two. Use a dictionary to find five more words in which 'bi' has this meaning.

    (a) _____

    (b) _____

    (c) _____

    (d) _____

    (e) _____

Letters into Words

3. Write three list words using the letters on the biceps.

    _____

    _____

    _____

Difficult words I have found	Practise	Practise

4. Use list and revision words to solve this crossword.

Across

4. Pair.

6. Resulting event.

7. Convince.

14. Pretend.

15. Music for two.

16. Able to speak two languages.

Down

1. Venture.

2. Arm muscles.

3. Counting system.

5. Trinkets.

8. Food intolerance.

9. Stress.

10. Two piece bathing suit.

11. Give up.

12. Twofold.

13. Fight between two people.

Word Worm Anagram

5. Circle the words in the word worm. Rearrange the remaining letters to make a word.

binaryiemphasiseallergysduobduetcprojectpdual

Magic Words

6. Change the first word into the last by changing one letter on each line to make a new word.

For example:　face　　(a) duel　　　　　　　　(b) dual

　　　　　　　　fact　　＿＿＿＿＿＿＿＿＿＿　　＿＿＿＿＿＿＿＿＿＿

　　　　　　　　tact　　＿＿＿＿＿＿＿＿＿＿　　＿＿＿＿＿＿＿＿＿＿

　　　　　　　　tack　　fill　　　　　　　　　　heap

List Words	Practise	Practise	D
tricycle			
triangle			
triple			
triplet			
octave			
octopus			
octane			
octagon			
column			
development			

Incorrect Words

1. Write the list words correctly.

   (a) tryangle _____

   (b) octapus _____

   (c) colum _____

   (d) octain _____

   (e) tripple _____

   (f) octogan _____

Rhyming Words

2. Find a word that rhymes.

   (a) ripple _____

   (b) grave _____

   (c) pain _____

   (d) wrangle _____

   (e) bicycle _____

   (f) pentagon _____

Missing Letters

3. Complete the list word.

   (a) __ __ i __ __ __

   (b) __ __ i __ __ __ __

   (c) __ __ i __ n __ __ __

   (d) __ __ i __ y __ __ __

Revision Words

physique	permit
queue	assignment
picturesque	propeller

Difficult words I have found	Practise	Practise

4. Find these list and revision words in the word search.

tricycle	octane
triplet	octave
triangle	octopus
triple	octagon
column	development
physique	permit
queue	assignment
picturesque	propeller

z	m	n	s	h	e	u	q	i	s	y	h	p
t	j	t	u	e	d	l	e	s	a	q	i	t
r	u	n	p	v	n	n	c	m	l	c	w	e
i	i	e	o	a	a	v	c	y	t	k	e	l
p	k	m	t	t	e	g	h	u	c	j	r	p
l	l	p	c	c	b	l	r	q	x	i	t	i
e	o	o	o	o	n	e	g	j	u	i	r	r
a	p	l	a	s	s	i	g	n	m	e	n	t
q	o	e	f	q	m	l	k	r	a	h	u	y
w	i	v	u	b	v	c	e	x	z	i	t	e
s	r	e	l	l	e	p	o	r	p	g	r	t
x	c	d	d	c	o	l	u	m	n	u	y	t
o	c	t	a	g	o	n	e	r	f	v	b	g

Missing Words

5. Use list or revision words to complete sentences.

(a) His mum would not _____ him to go on his

_____.

(b) In maths I had to calculate the areas of an _____ and a

_____.

(c) There was a _____ to sail round the _____ bay.

(d) There was some concern about the _____ of the third

_____.

(e) The journalist was encouraged to _____ the length of his

_____ in the newspaper.

(f) The marine biology student had to study an _____ for her

_____.

Extend Yourself

6. The word 'permit' can be used as a noun or a verb. Write a sentence for each.

(a) _____

_____

(b) _____

_____

List Words	Practise	Practise	D
decimal			
decimate			
decade			
decibel			
cent			
centre			
centimetre			
centigrade			
material			
heard			

All Mixed Up

1. Unjumble the list words.

   (a) greatniced _____

   (b) eatmiced _____

   (c) realmait _____

   (d) bedlice _____

   (e) emidlac _____

   (f) ntmereiect _____

Word Challenge

2. Make as many words as you can from letters in this word.

   centigrade

   _____

   _____

   _____

   _____

Mirror Writing

3. Write the mirror written words correctly.

   (a) heard _____

   (b) decimal _____

   (c) decade _____

   (d) centre _____

   (e) centimetre _____

Revision Words	
physical	window
equip	quality
benevolent	suspect

Difficult words I have found	Practise	Practise

Unit 5

4. Use list and revision words to solve this crossword.

Across

3. Annihilate.
4. It lets the light in.
7. Ten years.
10. Kit out.
14. Very generous.
15. Distrust.
16. Silk or cotton for example.

Down

1. Could be a measure of sound.
2. Detected by ear.
5. Counting in tens.
6. One hundredth of one euro.
8. Middle.
9. Worth.
11. To do with the body.
12. Celsius.
13. Ten millimetres.

Word Worm Anagram

5. Circle the words in the word worm. Rearrange the remaining letters to make a word.

Secret Code

6. Use the secret code to find out the list or revision word.

(a) _ _ _ _ _ _
   4 5 3 1 4 5

(b) _ _ _ _ _
   5 9 12 6 8

(c) _ _ _ _ _ _ _
   4 5 3 6 2 5 7

(d) _ _ _ _ _ _ _
   9 12 1 7 6 11 13

(e) _ _ _ _ _ _ _
   10 12 10 8 5 3 11

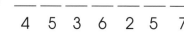

a	b	c	d	e	i	l	p	q	s	t	u	y
1	2	3	4	5	6	7	8	9	10	11	12	13

List Words	Practise	Practise	D
conserve			
confess			
conform			
congratulate			
exhaust			
exclude			
extreme			
exit			
assessment			
yesterday			

Small Words

1. Write the list word that contains these small words.

    (a) rat _____

    (b) for _____

    (c) yes _____

    (d) it _____

    (e) men _____

Verbs to Nouns

2. Change the verbs to nouns.

	Verb	Noun
(a)	exhaust	_____
(b)	congratulate	_____
(c)	exclude	_____
(d)	confess	_____
(e)	conserve	_____

Jumbled Words

3. Two list words are jumbled together. Write the two words.

    (a)   finesoxsect

    _____ + _____

    (b)   drovenexsulcece

    _____ + _____

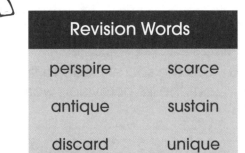

Revision Words	
perspire	scarce
antique	sustain
discard	unique

Difficult words I have found	Practise	Practise

4. Find these list and revision words in the word search.

conserve	extreme
conform	exhaust
congratulate	exclude
confess	exit
assessment	yesterday
perspire	scarce
antique	sustain
discard	unique

q	e	g	h	j	k	e	d	u	l	c	x	e
a	e	x	h	a	u	s	t	z	x	c	v	p
n	s	t	i	y	m	r	o	f	n	o	c	e
t	f	s	a	t	u	i	o	p	i	s	b	r
i	d	c	e	l	h	g	f	l	a	s	y	s
q	e	a	x	s	u	p	d	k	t	e	n	p
u	u	r	t	t	s	t	s	j	s	f	m	i
e	q	c	r	r	j	m	a	t	u	n	n	r
w	i	e	e	e	k	l	e	r	s	o	b	e
e	n	a	m	w	q	r	a	n	g	c	v	l
r	u	s	e	d	d	f	g	h	t	n	c	p
d	i	s	c	a	r	d	s	a	z	x	o	o
t	y	u	y	i	e	v	r	e	s	n	o	c

My Meanings

5. Write a definition for each of these words. Use a dictionary to check your answers.

(a) exhaust _____

(b) antique _____

(c) unique _____

(d) exclude _____

(e) sustain _____

(f) discard _____

Word Hunt

6. (a) Which word has five vowels? _____

(b) Which word can mean to obey? _____

(c) Find two rhyming words. _____ _____

(d) Which three words are nouns and verbs?

_____ _____ _____

(e) Which two words contain a mode of transport?

_____ _____

(f) Which two words contain an animal?

_____ _____

(g) Which word has two double consonants? _____

List Words	Practise	Practise	D
aerosol			
aerobics			
aeroplane			
aerospace			
aqualung			
aquatic			
aquarium			
aqueduct			
happened			
practise			

Prefixes

1. Choose the correct prefix to make the new words.

   aqua   aero

   (a) _____drome

   (b) _____marine

   (c) _____rius

   (d) _____nautics

   (e) _____batics

Letters into Words

3. Write three list words using the letters in the aquarium.

   (a) _____

   (b) _____

   (c) _____

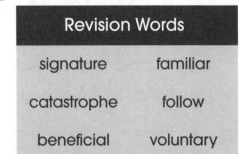

Shape Sorter

2. Write a word that fits in each shape.

   (a)

   (b)

   (c)

   (d)

   (e)

   (f)

Revision Words	
signature	familiar
catastrophe	follow
beneficial	voluntary

Difficult words I have found	Practise	Practise

4. Use list and revision words to solve this crossword.

Across

2. Disaster.
7. Flying machine.
8. Fish tank.
10. Spray can.
11. Autograph.
13. Advantageous.
15. Not compulsory.

Down

1. Rehearse.
3. To do with rockets.
4. Underwater breathing apparatus.

5. Occurred.
6. Waterway.
7. Marine.
9. Exercise class.
12. Well known.
14. Ensue.

Memory Master

5. (a) Cover the list and revision words. Write two from memory.

_____   _____

(b) Write one sentence using both words.

_____

_____

Mixed Up Sentences

6. Unjumble the sentences.

(a) was when catastrophe cracked. It the a aquarium

_____

(b) strict We programme of a in exercise aerobics follow class. our

_____

List Words	Practise	Practise	D
hydrotherapy			
hydrofoil			
hydrate			
hydrogen			
graph			
photograph			
autograph			
holograph			
jealous			
questionnaire			

Alphabetical Order

1. Put the words beginning with 'hy' in alphabetical order.

    (a) _____

    (b) _____

    (c) _____

    (d) _____

Sound Search

3. In the 'graph' words the 'ph' has the sound 'f'. Find five new words where 'ph' is pronounced 'f'.

    (a) _____

    (b) _____

    (c) _____

    (d) _____

    (e) _____

Secret Words

2. (a) Change 'hydro' to 'aroma' in hydrotherapy.

    _____

   (b) Change 'hydro' to 'aero' in hydrofoil.

    _____

   (c) Change 'auto' to 'tele' in autograph.

    _____

Revision Words	
Egypt	suspicion
widow	scarlet
quay	benefactor

Difficult words I have found	Practise	Practise

4. Find these list and revision words in the word search.

q	j	e	a	l	o	u	s	l	p	o	i	n
u	h	p	a	r	g	o	t	u	a	v	c	o
e	y	y	h	p	a	r	g	o	l	o	h	i
s	d	k	d	u	w	o	d	i	w	r	p	c
t	r	j	y	r	i	o	o	p	o	v	a	i
i	a	h	t	e	o	f	w	t	x	b	r	p
o	t	g	h	r	o	t	c	l	h	n	g	s
n	e	f	g	r	j	a	h	k	p	m	o	u
n	q	d	d	s	f	a	z	e	a	n	t	s
a	w	y	f	E	g	y	p	t	r	b	o	u
i	h	s	n	a	z	x	c	v	g	a	h	y
r	n	e	g	o	r	d	y	h	e	r	p	t
e	b	s	c	a	r	l	e	t	q	u	a	y

hydrogen   graph

hydrate   autograph

hydrotherapy   photograph

hydrofoil   holograph

jealous   questionnaire

Egypt   suspicion

widow   scarlet

quay   benefactor

Missing Words

5. Use the list or revision words to complete the sentences.

(a) The _____ took her husband's ashes to _____.

(b) The _____ indicated that they had used the gas,

_____ in the experiment.

(c) He is _____ because I have his favourite star's

_____.

(d) The _____ hit the _____
with a loud bang.

(e) My cousin is wearing a _____ dress in the wedding

_____.

Extend Yourself

6. Use a dictionary to find the meanings of these words.
Now write a sentence for each word.

hologram

(a) _____

_____

holograph

(b) _____

_____

Revision Unit 2

List Words	Practise	Practise	D
industrial			
received			
column			
development			
yesterday			
imaginary			
assessment			
consequence			
continuous			
practise			

All Mixed Up

1. Unjumble these revision words.

    (a) l o m u n c   _____

    (b) s t u c n o u n o i   _____

    (c) d i v e e c e r   _____

    (d) s t r a n d i l u i   _____

    (e) l e e v m e p o n d t   _____

    (f) d r y a y e s e t   _____

Missing Words

2. Complete using the revision words.

    (a) He had to _____ hard for his _____.

    (b) The little girl I saw _____ had an _____ friend.

    (c) The new _____ required the demolition of the ancient

    _____.

    (d) As a _____ of _____ action the mine closed.

Shape Sorter

3. Write a word that fits in the shape.

    (a) [shape]   (b) [shape]   (c) [shape]

4. Find 12 mistakes and write them correctly on the lines.

He has always   better at imaginery essays. He has, however, made a

_____

continnuous effort to practice the developement of a more serious writing

_____

style.   as a consequense, yestrday, he recieved word that his asessment,

_____

'Safety at Work', is to be published in the paper's industral colum.

_____

Word Hunt

5. (a) Which word has two double consonants?_____

(b) Which word has a silent 'n'?   _____

(c) Which words have five vowels?_____ _____

Alphabetical Order

6. Write all the revision words in alphabetical order.

_____

_____

_____

_____

Vertical Challenge

7. (a) Write the answers to each clue in the correct place, horizontally on the grid.

- Growth (11)
- Evaluation (10)
- Non-stop (10)
- Accepted (8)
- Pretend (9)
- Manufacturing (10)

(b) Write the word in the highlighted vertical column._____

(c) Write a clue for this word. _____

_____

List Words	Practise	Practise	D
audible			
audition			
audience			
auditory			
symbol			
symmetry			
sympathise			
symptom			
remember			
alcohol			

Incorrect Words

1. Write the list words correctly.

    (a)   simpathise _____

    (b)   ordible _____

    (c)   audiense _____

    (d)   remeber _____

    (e)   simbal _____

    (f)   alchohol _____

Rhyming Words

2. Find a word that rhymes.

    (a)   rendition _____

    (b)   empathise _____

    (c)   November _____

    (d)   protocol _____

    (e)   laudable _____

    (f)   thimble _____

    (g)   puppetry _____

Missing Letters

3. Complete the list word.

    (a)   __ y __ __ __ __ y

    (b)   __ y __ __ __ __ __

    (c)   __ y __ __ __ __ __ __ __

    (d)   __ y __ __ __ __

    (e)   __ __ __ __ __ __ y

Revision Words

moreover	monopoly
bilingual	triple
cent	conserve

Difficult words I have found	Practise	Practise

4. Use list and revision words to solve this crossword.

Across

2. Spectators.

5. Liquid produced by fermentation.

9. One side mirroring the other.

11. Recall.

13. Threefold.

14. Trial for a role.

15. To do with hearing.

Down

1. Able to be heard.

3. Protect from harm.

4. Speaking two languages.

6. Feel sorry for.

7. Icon.

8. One hundredth of a euro.

9. Sign of illness.

10. And also.

12. Sole ownership.

Word Worm Anagram

5. Find the four words that are written backwards and unjumble the remaining letters to make a fifth word.

elbiduaprlaugnilibetlohoclalievresnoc

Homophones

6. Circle and write the correct word.

(a) I sent/cent the dented symbol/cymbal to be repaired.

_____   _____

(b) There is a symbol/cymbal on every sent/cent.

_____   _____

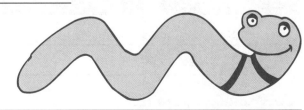

List Words	Practise	Practise	D
portable			
export			
portrait			
import			
primary			
primitive			
primate			
primarily			
technique			
proposition			

All Mixed Up

1. Unjumble the list words.

   (a) t i m v e p i r i   _____

   (b) n o t p o o r i s p i _____

   (c) t o r t a p i r   _____

   (d) p a r t i m e   _____

   (e) e i c h q t n e u   _____

   (f) x p r e o t   _____

Word Challenge

2. Make as many words as you can from letters in this word.

   portable

   _____

   _____

   _____

   _____

   _____

Small Words

3. Write the list word that contains these small words.

   (a) sit _____

   (b) imp _____

   (c) mat _____

   (d) tab _____

Revision Words	
aerosol	hydrogen
whatever	university
bikini	triplet

Difficult words I have found	Practise	Practise

Unit 10 port prim

4. Find these list and revision words in the word search.

portable   primary

portrait   primate

import   primitive

export   primarily

technique   proposition

aerosol   hydrogen

whatever   university

bikini   triplet

q	j	k	w	h	a	t	e	v	e	r	l	p
p	r	i	m	a	t	e	u	n	m	n	b	t
r	r	m	j	a	h	g	q	u	f	d	v	i
i	h	o	k	e	a	q	i	n	w	s	c	a
m	y	n	p	r	s	i	n	i	k	i	b	r
i	l	e	l	o	d	g	h	v	e	a	x	t
t	i	g	p	s	s	f	c	e	r	z	e	r
i	r	o	o	o	f	i	e	r	r	l	x	o
v	a	r	i	l	y	t	t	s	p	x	p	p
e	m	d	u	y	r	a	m	i	r	p	o	m
w	i	y	n	b	v	c	r	t	o	z	r	i
e	r	h	g	f	d	t	s	y	a	n	t	o
r	p	o	r	t	a	b	l	e	t	y	u	i

Sentences

5. Write each of these words in a sentence.

(a) technique _____

_____

(b) proposition _____

_____

(c) primate _____

_____

(d) export _____

_____

Secret Code

6. Use the secret code to find the list or revision word.

(a) __ __ __ __ __ __
   2 14 9 8 10 11

(b) __ __ __ __ __ __ __
   11 10 4 9 5 2 11

(c) __ __ __ __ __ __ __ __
   13 3 1 11 2 12 2 10

(d) __ __ __ __ __ __ __ __
   9 8 10 11 10 1 4 11

a	e	h	i	l	m	n	o	p	r	t	v	w	x	y
1	2	3	4	5	6	7	8	9	10	11	12	13	14	15

List Words	Practise	Practise	D
scope			
stethoscope			
horoscope			
periscope			
scribe			
prescribe			
scribble			
describe			
enquire			
improvise			

Verbs to Nouns

1. Complete the table. You may use a dictionary.

	Verb	Noun
(a)	prescribe	_____
(b)	enquire	_____
(c)	improvise	_____
(d)	describe	_____

Suffixes

2. Choose the correct suffix to make new words.

scope   scribe

(a) gyro_____
(b) trans_____
(c) tele_____
(d) sub_____
(e) micro_____

Jumbled Words

3. Two list words are jumbled together. Write the two words.

(a)   cospherecopsoo

_____ + _____

(b)   ripebicepscoblers

_____ + _____

Revision Words

centimetre	congratulate
aqualung	graph
consequently	universal

Difficult words I have found	Practise	Practise

4. Use list and revision words to solve this crossword.

Across

1. Meaningless marks.
3. It tells your future.
4. Say what it is like.
6. A submarine has this.
9. As a result of.
10. Make up.
12. World wide.
13. Picture of results.
14. Used to listen to breathing and your heart.

Down

1. He writes for someone.
2. Range.
5. A small measure.
6. Set down.
7. Say, 'Well done'.
8. Ask.
11. Breathing apparatus.

Memory Master

5. (a) Cover the list and revision words. Write two from memory.

_____   _____

(b) Write one sentence using both words.

_____

_____

Mixed Up Sentences

6. Unjumble the sentences.

(a) what Can like ? describe stethoscope a you looks

_____

(b) stored beside the the The periscope. in was aqualung cupboard

_____

List Words	Practise	Practise	D
submarine			
subway			
subsidy			
subterfuge			
supermarket			
superior			
superficial			
superimpose			
technology			
murmur			

Alphabetical Order

1. Put the words beginning with 'su' in alphabetical order.

   _____

   _____

   _____

   _____

   _____

   _____

Mirror Writing

2. Write the mirror written words correctly.

   (a) superior   _____

   (b) murmur   _____

   (c) technology   _____

   (d) subsidy   _____

   (e) subterfuge   _____

   (f) submarine   _____

   (g) superficial   _____

Letters into Words

3. Write three list words using the letters on the submarine.

   _____

   _____

   _____

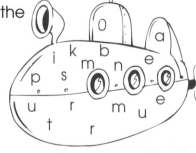

Revision Words	
binary	triangle
centigrade	confess
aerobics	hydrofoil

Difficult words I have found	Practise	Practise	

4. Find these list and revision words in the word search.

submarine   supermarket

subsidy   superficial

subterfuge   superior

subway   superimpose

technology   murmur

binary   triangle

centigrade   confess

aerobics   hydrofoil

s	s	s	s	u	b	t	e	r	f	u	g	e
c	u	u	u	e	l	y	h	n	b	g	r	t
i	b	p	p	d	a	y	a	w	b	u	s	t
b	s	e	e	a	i	w	e	r	m	t	t	e
o	i	r	r	r	c	q	b	r	n	r	n	c
r	d	i	m	g	i	a	u	a	m	i	y	h
e	y	o	a	i	f	m	v	z	r	a	u	n
a	r	r	r	t	r	s	p	a	l	n	i	o
q	a	u	k	n	e	d	m	o	k	g	o	l
a	n	j	e	e	p	b	c	x	s	l	p	o
z	i	m	t	c	u	f	g	h	j	e	l	g
x	b	k	i	s	s	e	f	n	o	c	o	y
h	y	d	r	o	f	o	i	l	c	d	e	r

My Meanings

5. Write a definition for each of these words.
Use a dictionary to check your answers.

(a) aerobics _____

(b) superficial _____

(c) hydrofoil _____

(d) subterfuge _____

(e) subsidy _____

(f) superimpose _____

_____

Word Hunt

6. (a) Which word has a silent 'h'? _____

(b) Which two words are compound words?

_____ _____

(c) Find three words with two syllables. _____

_____ _____

(d) Which word is an antonym of 'inferior'? _____

(e) Which two words are forms of water transport?

_____ _____

List Words	Practise	Practise	D
obtain			
oblige			
obstruct			
obstinate			
witch			
switch			
stitch			
crutch			
prioritise			
potential			

Incorrect Words

1. Write the list words correctly.

    (a) whitch   _____

    (b) potencial _____

    (c) oblije   _____

    (d) obtane   _____

    (e) obstenate _____

    (f) proirtise _____

Secret Words

2. (a) Change 'ise' to 'ies' in prioritise.

        _____

    (b) Change 'ob' to 'de' in obtain.

        _____

    (c) Change 'ge' to 'que' in oblige.

        _____

    (d) Change 'pot' to 'ess' in potential.

        _____

Missing Letters

3. Complete the list word.

    (a) __ t __ t __ __

    (b) __ __ __ t __ __ __ t __ __ __

    (c) __ __ t __ __ t __ __ __

    (d) __ __ t __ __

    (e) __ __ __ t __ __ __ t __

Revision Words		
since	monotone	biceps
octave	decade	aerospace

Difficult words I have found	Practise	Practise

4. Use list and revision words to solve this crossword.

Across

3. Possible achievement.

7. Swap.

9. From that time.

10. Acquire.

11. To do with rockets.

13. Sew.

14. Ten years.

15. Support when you are lame.

16. She casts spells.

Down

1. Unchanging sound.

2. Help out.

4. Stubborn.

5. Put to the fore.

6. Eight notes.

8. Muscles in the arm.

12. Hinder.

Missing Words

5. Use list or revision words to complete sentences.

(a) Can you _____ chords to a higher _____?

(b) The saboteur did his best to _____ the _____ programme.

(c) In that _____ a _____ would have been burned at the stake.

(d) _____ my unfortunate accident, I have had to use a

_____.

Word Worm Anagram

6. Find the four words that are written backwards and unjumble the remaining letters to make a fifth word.

List Words	Practise	Practise	D
poster			
postmortem			
posterity			
postpone			
credible			
incredible			
credit			
credentials			
evaluation			
stomach			

All Mixed Up

1. Unjumble the list words

   (a) c r l i e i n b e d _____

   (b) n o p e p o t s _____

   (c) p o t t o r s e m m _____

   (d) h o t c a s m _____

   (e) v u a t e a l n o i _____

Synonyms

3. Find a list word with a similar meaning.

   (a) autopsy _____

   (b) assessment _____

   (c) abdomen _____

   (d) believable _____

   (e) praise _____

   (f) amazing _____

Word Challenge

2. Make as many words as you can from letters in this word.

   credentials

   _____

   _____

   _____

   _____

   _____

   _____

   _____

Revision Words	
photograph	octagon
nonetheless	union
decimate	aquarium

Difficult words I have found	Practise	Practise

4. Find these list and revision words in the word search.

poster

posterity

postmortem

postpone

evaluation

photograph

nonetheless

decimate

credit

incredible

credible

credentials

stomach

octagon

union

aquarium

a	q	u	a	r	i	u	m	o	i	u	y	t
p	l	p	p	x	z	p	r	e	t	s	o	p
n	h	p	o	z	o	o	a	l	s	d	f	s
o	x	o	s	a	c	s	x	b	c	d	s	l
i	c	s	t	s	t	k	i	v	e	t	a
n	v	t	p	o	a	m	j	d	l	c	o	i
u	m	e	o	d	g	o	h	e	b	i	m	t
t	b	r	n	f	o	r	h	r	n	m	a	n
i	n	i	e	g	n	t	a	c	m	a	c	e
d	q	t	c	v	e	e	b	p	n	t	h	d
e	w	y	l	n	k	m	j	h	h	e	g	e
r	e	n	o	i	t	a	u	l	a	v	e	r
c	i	n	c	r	e	d	i	b	l	e	r	c

Secret Code

5. Use the secret code to find the list or revision word.

(a) __ __ __ __ __ __
2 11 4 3 7 13

(b) __ __ __ __ __
14 8 7 9 8

(c) __ __ __ __ __ __ __
9 2 13 1 5 9 8

(d) __ __ __ __ __ __ __ __
10 9 12 13 10 9 8 4

(e) __ __ __ __ __ __
10 9 12 13 4 11

(f) __ __ __ __ __ __ __ __ __ __
10 6 9 13 9 5 11 1 10 6

a	c	d	e	g	h	i	n	o	p	r	s	t	u
1	2	3	4	5	6	7	8	9	10	11	12	13	14

Extend Yourself

6. Use a dictionary to find three more words with the prefix 'post'. Write a sentence for each word.

(a) _____

_____

(b) _____

_____

(c) _____

_____

List Words	Practise	Practise	D
spectacle			
specialist			
speculate			
spectator			
uphold			
upstairs			
upright			
upkeep			
processor			
strategy			

Jumbled Words

1. Two list words are jumbled together. Write the two words.

    (a)   kageuttyepsrep

    _____ + _____

    (b)   couldpealshupte

    _____ + _____

Rhyming Words

3. Find a word that rhymes.

    (a) accumulate _____

    (b) tragedy _____

    (c) receptacle _____

    (d) flares _____

    (e) professor _____

    (f) bright _____

    (g) regulator _____

Small Words

2. Write the list word that contains these small words.

    (a) rat _____

    (b) old _____

    (c) is _____

    (d) air _____

    (e) ate _____

    (f) rig _____

    (g) so _____

Revision Words

octopus	monologue
centre	conform
hydrotherapy	exhaust

Difficult words I have found	Practise	Practise

4. Use list and revision words to solve this crossword.

Across

3.   Water treatment.

4.   Tire out.

6.   Expert.

7.   Viewer.

11. A sight.

13. Speech for one.

14. Maintenance.

15. Middle.

Down

1.   Food mixer.

2.   Plan.

5.   Erect.

6.   Consider.

8.   It has eight tentacles.

9.   First floor.

10. Sustain.

12. Obey the rules.

Sentences

5. Write each of these words in a sentence.

(a)   speculate _____

_____

(b)   monologue _____

_____

Memory Master

6. (a)   Cover the list and revision words. Write three from memory.

_____   _____   _____

(b)   For each word, write a question that has the word as its answer.

(i) _____

(ii) _____

(iii) _____

List Words	Practise	Practise	D
concede			
recede			
precede			
intercede			
include			
secluded			
conclude			
preclude			
marriage			
buried			

Alphabetical Order

1. Put the words with the pattern 'cede' in alphabetical order.

   (a) _____

   (b) _____

   (c) _____

   (d) _____

Verbs to Nouns

2. Complete the table. You may use a dictionary.

         Verb   Noun

   (a) recede   _____

   (b) include   _____

   (c) conclude   _____

   (d) concede   _____

Mirror Writing

3. Write the mirror written words correctly.

   (a) marriage _____

   (b) secluded _____

   (c) intercede _____

   (d) buried _____

   (e) conclude _____

   (f) include _____

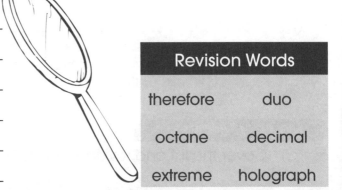

Revision Words	
therefore	duo
octane	decimal
extreme	holograph

Difficult words I have found	Practise	Practise

4. Find these list and revision words in the word search.

concede	conclude
precede	include
recede	secluded
intercede	preclude
marriage	buried
therefore	duo
octane	decimal
extreme	holograph

t	p	l	k	j	h	p	g	f	d	s	a	z
h	o	e	d	e	c	r	e	t	n	i	s	b
e	o	c	t	a	n	e	o	p	l	m	d	u
r	i	l	a	i	e	c	c	o	m	a	f	r
e	u	p	o	u	x	e	u	z	m	r	g	i
f	y	r	d	g	t	d	v	a	n	r	h	e
o	t	e	e	y	r	e	l	q	b	i	j	d
r	r	c	d	t	e	a	d	w	v	a	k	u
e	e	l	u	r	m	e	p	e	c	g	l	l
m	w	u	l	i	e	z	x	h	c	e	p	c
n	q	d	c	o	n	c	e	d	e	e	o	n
b	q	e	e	w	e	r	t	y	u	i	r	o
v	d	c	s	x	e	d	u	l	c	n	i	c

My Meanings

5. Write a definition for each of these words. Use a dictionary to check your answers.

(a) secluded _____

(b) octane _____

(c) extreme _____

(d) intercede _____

(e) conclude _____

Mixed Up Sentences

6. Unjumble the sentences.

(a) had man. were remains a conclude age that the They to buried of stone

_____

(b) holograph in alcove library. was a secluded found in The the

_____

(c) will crowd if recede. The does intercede protesting the army not

_____

(d) include their The songs duo new will all in favourite album. their

_____

Revision Unit 3

List Words	Practise	Practise	D
prioritise			
proposition			
improvise			
murmur			
potential			
marriage			
buried			
technique			
stomach			
enquire			

All Mixed Up

1. Unjumble these revision words.

   (a) n o p o s t r i p i o _____

   (b) a g r i m r a e _____

   (c) u b i r e d _____

   (d) n e t i l a p o t _____

   (e) n i q u r e e _____

   (f) s i p o v m i r e _____

Shape Sorter

2. Write a word that fits in the shape.

   (a)

   (b)

   (c)

   CSAER

Missing Words

3. Complete using the revision words.

   (a) You will increase your _____ if you _____ at work.

   (b) Although she had considered _____, she refused his _____.

   (c) When that _____ failed we had to _____.

   (d) The pirate heard a _____ about _____ treasure.

   (e) I would like to _____ whether you feel better after the _____ ache.

4. Find 12 mistakes and write them correctly on the lines.

> After accepting his proposation of marrage she heard a murmir that he had
>
> _____
>
> a potentally fatal stumach problem. She went   enquier and was told that
>
> _____
>
> her husband must prioratise and impravise   necessary, to decrease his
>
> _____
>
> workload. This technic did not work and he was soon dead and bureed.
>
> _____

Word Hunt

5. (a) Which word contains a small word that names a number?_____

(b) Which two words have a silent 'h'?

_____   _____

(c) Which word can be a verb or a noun?_____

Alphabetical Order

6. Write all the revision words in alphabetical order.

_____

_____

_____

Vertical Challenge

7. (a) Write the answers to each clue in the correct place, horizontally on the grid.

- Interred (6)
- Make do (9)
- Put first (10)
- Ask (7)
- Abdomen (7)
- Wedding (8)

(b) Write the word in the highlighted vertical column. _____

(c) Write a clue for this word. _____

_____

List Words	Practise	Practise	D
definite			
environment			
secretary			
cupboard			
vegetable			
raspberry			
benefit			
government			
diary			
issue			

Incorrect Words

1. Write the list words correctly.

   (a) defnite   _____

   (b) dairy   _____

   (c) secrtary   _____

   (d) vegetible   _____

   (e) cuboard   _____

   (f) benifit   _____

Secret Words

2. (a) Change 'rasp' to 'straw' in raspberry.

   _____

   (b) Change 'vege' to 'adap' in vegetable.

   _____

   (c) Change 'cup' to 'bill' in cupboard.

   _____

Letters into Words

3. Write three list words using the letters on the raspberry.

   _____

   _____

   _____

Revision Words	
audible	portrait
scribe	subway
stitch	incredible

Difficult words I have found	Practise	Practise

4. Use list and revision words to solve this crossword.

Across

3.   Advantage.

6.   Extraordinary.

9.   Group who run the country.

11.   Concern.

13.   Store things here.

14.   Typist for the boss.

15.   Perceptible.

Down

1.   A painting.

2.   Certain.

4.   Book recording events.

5.   Edible roots or leaves.

7.   Surroundings.

8.   Soft red fruit.

10.   Writer.

12.   Mend.

14. Underground railway.

Missing Words

5. Use list or revision words to complete sentences.

(a) The _____ official forgot to _____ the permit.

(b) Let's have the _____ curry that's in the _____.

(c) That pollution will have a _____ impact on the

_____.

(d) We heard the _____ news that the _____ is to close.

Word Worm Anagram

6. Find the four words that are written backwards and unjumble the remaining letters to make a fifth word.

tiartropfniyraidtedraobpucedielbidua

List Words	Practise	Practise	D
adventure			
departure			
puncture			
fixture			
fountain			
certain			
abstain			
contain			
evidence			
actually			

Word Challenge

1. Make as many words as you can from letters in this word.

   departure

   _____

   _____

   _____

   _____

Revision Words

upkeep

conclude

export

spectacle

stethoscope

superficial

Missing Letters

2. Complete the list word.

   (a) __ o __ __ a i __

   (b) a __ __ u a __ __ __

   (c) __ i __ __ u __ e

   (d) __ o u __ __ a i __

   (e) __ u __ __ __ u __ e

   (f) a __ __ e __ __ u __ e

   (g) __ e __ __ __ __ __

   (h) e __ i __ e __ __ e

Phrases

3. Add a list word to make a common phrase.

   (a) _____ kit

   (b) _____ lounge

   (c) dead _____

   (d) false _____

   (e) _____ playground

Difficult words I have found	Practise	Practise

4. Find these list and revision words in the word search.

adventure   departure

puncture   fixture

fountain   certain

abstain   contain

evidence   actually

upkeep   conclude

export   spectacle

stethoscope   superficial

a	d	v	e	n	t	u	r	e	j	h	g	f
s	k	t	y	u	a	c	t	u	a	l	l	y
c	t	r	u	n	i	a	t	s	b	a	i	d
o	f	e	f	o	u	n	t	a	i	n	o	e
n	i	e	t	d	f	g	h	c	y	e	l	p
c	x	r	p	h	b	v	i	j	t	c	n	a
l	t	u	e	s	o	f	c	k	a	n	i	r
u	u	t	e	a	r	s	x	t	r	e	a	t
d	r	c	k	e	a	z	c	l	e	d	t	u
e	e	n	p	i	o	e	p	o	w	i	n	r
m	l	u	u	e	p	w	q	q	p	v	o	e
n	s	p	p	s	n	i	a	t	r	e	c	d
b	v	c	e	x	p	o	r	t	x	z	a	s

Extend Yourself

5. Find three more words with the suffix 'tain'.
Write a sentence for each word.

(a) _____

_____

(b) _____

_____

(c) _____

_____

Secret Code

6. Use the secret code to find the list or revision word.

(a) __ __ __ __ __ __
   3 14 9 8 10 12

(b) __ __ __ __ __ __ __
   2 3 10 12 1 5 7

(c) __ __ __ __ __ __ __
   4 5 14 12 13 10 3

(d) __ __ __ __ __ __ __ __
   9 13 7 2 12 13 10 3

(e) __ __ __ __ __ __ __ __ __ __ __
  11 13 9 3 10 4 5 2 5 1 6

(f) __ __ __ __ __ __ __
   2 8 7 12 1 5 7

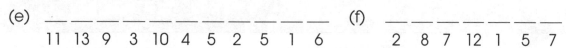

a	c	e	f	i	l	n	o	p	r	s	t	u	x
1	2	3	4	5	6	7	8	9	10	11	12	13	14

List Words	Practise	Practise	D
saucer			
astronaut			
dinosaur			
laundry			
swarm			
thwart			
award			
wardrobe			
lonely			
analysis			

All Mixed Up

1. Unjumble the list words.

   (a) n o u s r a i d _____

   (b) d r a w b o r e _____

   (c) a c r u s e _____

   (d) n o e l l y _____

   (e) h a w r t t _____

Mirror Writing

2. Write the mirror written words correctly.

   (a) thwart _____

   (b) analysis _____

   (c) laundry _____

   (d) astronaut _____

   (e) swarm _____

   (f) saucer _____

   (g) award _____

   (h) dinosaur _____

Small Words

3. Write the list word that contains these small words.

   (a) art _____

   (b) din _____

   (c) rob _____

   (d) dry _____

   (e) one _____

   (f) arm _____

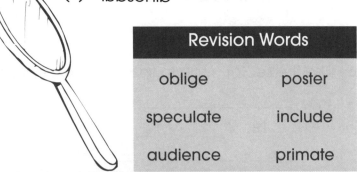

Revision Words

oblige	poster
speculate	include
audience	primate

Difficult words I have found	Practise	Practise

4. Use list and revision words to solve the crossword.

Across

2.   Extinct animal.

5.   Put in.

7.   Monkey.

10. Spaceman.

11. Collection of clothes.

13. Prevent.

14. Plate for a cup.

15. A large notice.

Down

1.   Detailed examination.

3.   Do a favour for.

4.   Prize.

6.   Form opinions

8.   By yourself and sad.

9.   Group of insects.

10. Spectators.

12. Where clothes are washed.

Memory Master

5. (a) Cover the list and revision words. Write three from memory.

_____   _____   _____

(b) For each word, write a question that has the word as its answer.

(i) _____

(ii) _____

(iii)_____

Sentences

6. Write each of these words in a sentence.

(a) thwart _____

_____

(b) analysis _____

_____

(c) speculate _____

_____

List Words	Practise	Practise	D
rogue			
revenue			
subdue			
continue			
petrol			
enrol			
carol			
revolve			
surely			
permanent			

Alphabetical Order

1. Put the words with the pattern 'ue' in alphabetical order.

   (a) _____

   (b) _____

   (c) _____

   (d) _____

Jumbled Words

3. Two list words are jumbled together. Write the two words.

   (a)   verysurevello

   _____ + _____

   (b)   poorglueter

   _____ + _____

   (c)   emaclprtaronen

   _____ + _____

Rhyming Words

2. Find a word that rhymes with:

   (a) vogue   _____

   (b) solve   _____

   (c) purely   _____

   (d) patrol   _____

   (e) review   _____

   (f) barrel   _____

Revision Words	
periscope	subsidy
obstinate	posterity
credentials	audition

Difficult words I have found	Practise	Practise

4. Find these list and revision words in the word search.

rogue   carol

revenue   petrol

subdue   enrol

continue   revolve

surely   permanent

periscope   subsidy

obstinate   posterity

credentials   audition

m	s	r	e	v	e	n	u	e	j	h	g	f
n	u	k	u	p	e	r	m	a	n	e	n	t
r	b	l	a	c	o	y	l	e	r	u	s	s
e	d	p	i	u	z	c	a	s	d	l	y	u
v	u	l	e	l	d	l	s	p	a	d	t	b
o	e	o	o	t	l	i	s	i	o	f	r	s
l	u	r	r	q	a	a	t	d	r	g	e	i
v	n	t	o	w	k	n	d	i	i	e	w	d
e	i	e	g	e	e	h	i	f	o	h	p	y
b	t	p	u	d	r	t	y	t	u	n	q	d
v	n	o	e	o	u	p	l	k	s	j	w	s
l	o	r	a	c	i	u	y	t	r	b	e	a
c	c	x	z	y	t	i	r	e	t	s	o	p

Mixed Up Sentences

5. Unjumble the sentences. Add a capital letter and a full stop.

(a)   car could the of our continue not petrol journey out as we ran

_____

(b)   false tried using country the the credentials enter to rogue

_____

(c)   his obstinate permanent the scowl boy on has a face

_____

(d)   company received the subsidy they got some the from government more from the revenue

_____

Magic Words

6. Change the first word into the last by changing one letter on each line to make a new word.

For example: thick   (a)   rogue   (b)   petrol

                trick   _____   _____

                track   _____   _____

                trace   value   matron

List Words	Practise	Practise	D
criticism			
optimism			
pessimism			
hypnotism			
feminist			
atheist			
egotist			
tourist			
design			
participation			

Incorrect Words

1. Write the list words correctly.

(a) hipnotism _____

(b) critisism _____

(c) pesimism _____

(d) femmimist _____

(e) optimmism _____

(f) affeist _____

(g) eggotist _____

Nouns to Verbs

2. Change the nouns to verbs.

Nouns   Verbs

(a) criticism   _____

(b) hypnotism _____

(c) participation _____

Revision Words

symmetry   scribble

superimpose   switch

uphold   sympathise

Letters into Words

3. Write three list words using the letters on the design.

_____

_____

_____

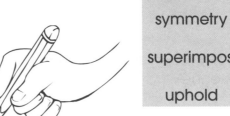

Difficult words I have found	Practise	Practise

4. Use list and revision words to solve this crossword.

Across

1. _____ can help you remember.
3. Taking part.
6. Support a decision or belief.
10. Where one half of a figure mirrors the other.
12. An _____ believes he is more important than others.
13. Someone who believes in equality for women.
14. Swap.

Down

2. Put something on top of something else.
3. Believing bad things will happen.
4. A person visiting a place for pleasure.
5. Finding fault.
7. Hopefulness about the future.
8. Plan.
9. Care about someone else's problems.
10. Write untidily.
11. A person who believes there is no god.

Missing Words

5. Use list or revision words to complete sentences.

(a) The _____ failed because of poor _____ on the part of the client.

(b) An _____ does not _____ any religious beliefs.

(c) The _____ was full of _____ about the success of his trip.

Word Worm Anagram

6. Find the four words that are written backwards and unjumble the remaining letters to make a fifth word.

esihtapmystsngisedhwtsitogecielbbircs

List Words	Practise	Practise	D
restaurant			
blouse			
bulletin			
jodhpurs			
balcony			
pizza			
patio			
hurricane			
outrageous			
relief			

Word Challenge

1. Make as many words as you can from letters in this word.

   outrageous

   _____

   _____

   _____

   _____

Small Words

2. Write the list word that contains these small words.

   (a) can   _____

   (b) rag   _____

   (c) let   _____

   (d) lie   _____

   (e) ant   _____

   (f) con   _____

   (g) at   _____

Missing Letters

3. Complete these list words.

   (a) __ u __ __ __ __ __ __ __

   (b) __ __ __ __ __ u __ __

   (c) __ u __ __ __ __ __ __ u __

   (d) __ u __ __ __ __ __

   (e) __ __ __ __ __ u __ __ __

Revision Words	
primary	subterfuge
obtain	postmortem
specialist	intercede

Difficult words I have found	Practise	Practise

4. Find these list and revision words in the word search.

restaurant   blouse

bulletin   jodhpurs

balcony   pizza

patio   hurricane

outrageous   relief

primary   subterfuge

obtain   postmortem

specialist   intercede

b	a	l	c	o	n	y	r	a	m	i	r	p
m	m	o	p	l	k	j	h	g	f	d	s	a
n	i	e	f	e	d	e	c	r	e	t	n	i
b	u	e	t	e	i	u	y	t	r	s	e	z
v	y	g	o	r	i	z	a	s	u	i	w	x
n	t	u	p	x	o	l	b	o	s	l	q	j
i	t	f	l	c	i	m	e	v	d	a	b	o
t	n	r	k	v	t	g	t	r	d	i	l	d
e	i	e	j	j	a	h	g	s	f	c	o	p
l	a	t	r	r	p	e	w	q	o	e	u	h
l	t	b	t	c	x	a	z	z	i	p	s	u
u	b	u	t	n	a	r	u	a	t	s	e	r
b	o	s	h	u	r	r	i	c	a	n	e	s

Secret Code

5. Use the secret code to find the list or revision word.

(a) __ __ __ __ __ __
   2 6 8 12 10 4

(b) __ __ __ __ __ __ __
   2 1 6 3 8 7 13

(c) __ __ __ __ __ __
   8 2 11 1 5 7

(d) __ __ __ __ __
   9 1 11 5 8

(e) __ __ __ __ __
   9 5 14 14 1

(f) __ __ __ __ __ __ __
   2 12 6 6 4 11 5 7

a	b	c	e	i	l	n	o	p	s	t	u	y	z
1	2	3	4	5	6	7	8	9	10	11	12	13	14

Extend Yourself

6. Use a dictionary to find the meanings of these words. Write a sentence for each word.

(a) jodhpurs _____

_____

(b) subterfuge _____

_____

(c) bulletin _____

_____

(d) outrageous _____

_____

List Words	Practise	Practise	D
sensory			
laboratory			
history			
dormitory			
fury			
injury			
treasury			
century			
interrupt			
soldier			

All Mixed Up

1. Unjumble the list words.

   (a) a s u r e t r y _____

   (b) r o o m t i d y r _____

   (c) p u t r e n t i r _____

   (d) d r o l i e s _____

Plurals

3. Write the plurals of these singular nouns.

	Singular	Plural
(a)	laboratory	_____
(b)	dormitory	_____
(c)	treasury	_____
(d)	injury	_____
(e)	century	_____
(f)	soldier	_____

Mirror Writing

2. Write the mirror written words correctly.

   (a) laboratory _____

   (b) history _____

   (c) sensory _____

   (d) century _____

   (e) fury _____

   (f) dormitory _____

   (g) soldier _____

Revision Words	
primitive	concede
horoscope	obstruct
supermarket	upright

Difficult words I have found	Practise	Practise

4. Use list and revision words to solve this crossword.

Across

1. Fighter.
6. Grocery store.
11. Hinder.
12. A bedroom for many people.
14. Wound.
15. Funds.
16. Times past.

Down

2. Science room.
3. Star sign prediction.
4. Give in.
5. A hundred years.
7. Ancient.
8. Disrupt.
9. To do with the senses.
10. Erect.
13. Rage.

Word Hunt

5. (a) Which words have a soft 'c'? _____ _____

(b) Which two words are compound words?

_____ _____

(c) Which word contains a small word that names a rodent?

_____

(d) Which word contains a small word that can be found in a famous Bible story?

_____

Memory Master

6. (a) Cover the list and revision words. Write three from memory.

_____ _____

(b) For each word, write a question that has the word as its answer.

(i) _____

(ii) _____

(iii) _____

List Words	Practise	Practise	D
author			
escalator			
calculator			
solicitor			
gateau			
plateau			
chateau			
bureau			
embarrass			
sincerely			

Alphabetical Order

1. Put the words with the pattern 'or' in alphabetical order.

   (a) _____

   (b) _____

   (c) _____

   (d) _____

Plurals

2. Write the plural of these singular nouns.

	Singular	Plural
(a)	chateau	_____
(b)	plateau	_____
(c)	gateau	_____
(d)	bureau	_____

Jumbled Words

3. Two list words are jumbled together. Write the two words.

   (a)   ahutheartcuao

   _____ + _____

   (b)   eugetacarnisely

   _____ + _____

   (c)   uoibutsreioacrl

   _____ + _____

Revision Words	
secluded	auditory
portable	superior
witch	credit

Difficult words I have found	Practise	Practise

4. Find these list and revision words in the word search.

calculator chateau

author gateau

escalator plateau

solicitor bureau

embarrass sincerely

secluded auditory

portable superior

witch credit

q	f	s	y	r	o	t	i	d	u	a	v	c
a	r	i	s	s	o	l	i	c	i	t	o	r
c	t	l	u	i	k	t	i	d	e	r	c	d
h	a	o	s	a	n	f	a	d	s	a	s	e
a	u	l	e	g	e	c	z	l	x	s	m	r
t	t	p	c	h	q	t	e	y	a	q	j	o
e	h	o	l	u	w	u	a	r	c	c	u	i
a	o	h	u	j	l	i	r	g	e	w	s	r
u	r	c	d	k	e	a	r	t	v	l	y	e
z	g	t	e	l	b	m	t	n	b	e	y	p
x	b	i	d	m	i	u	y	o	t	r	h	u
s	n	w	e	e	l	b	a	t	r	o	p	s
p	l	a	t	e	a	u	a	e	r	u	b	w

My Meanings

5. Write a definition for each of these words.
Use a dictionary to check your answers.

(a) auditory_____

(b) plateau _____

(c) superior _____

(d) solicitor _____

(e) secluded _____

(f) credit _____

(g) author_____

(h) escalator_____

Word Worm Anagram

6. Find the four words that are written backwards and unjumble the remaining letters to make a fifth word.

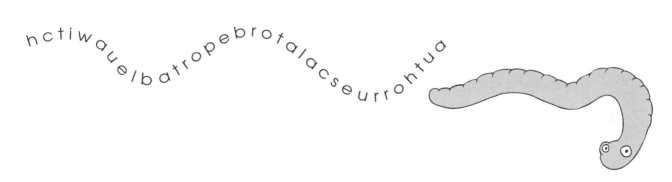

Revision Unit 4

List Words	Practise	Practise	D
diary			
evidence			
analysis			
permanent			
participation			
soldier			
lonely			
outrageous			
embarrass			
issue			

All Mixed Up

1. Unjumble these revision words.

   (a) y e l l o n   _____

   (b) s i l y s a n a   _____

   (c) s e t a g o u r o u   _____

   (d) d i n e c e v e   _____

   (e) t a p m e n n e r   _____

   (f) r e d l i o s   _____

   (g) s e u i s   _____

   (h) m b s a r e a r s   _____

Shape Sorter

2. Write a word that fits in the shape.

   (a)

   (b)

   (c)

   (d)

   (e)

   (f)

Missing Words

3. Complete using the revision words.

   (a) You will _____ your mother with your _____ behaviour.

   (b) The school board will _____ an academic

   _____ to each teacher.

   (c) The detective uncovered _____ of his _____ in the crime.

   (d) The _____ found the night watch a particularly

   _____ duty.

4. Find 12 mistakes and write them correctly on the lines.

> An analisis of the entry in the dairy of the lonly soljier revealed permenant
>
> edivence about the isue of his death   everyone in the barracks knew that it
>
> would embarass the major when his partisipation in the outrageus crime was
>
> revealed.

Word Hunt

5. (a) Which word has two double consonants? _____

(b) Which word has five syllables? _____

(c) Which word means the opposite of temporary? _____

Alphabetical Order

6. Write all the revision words in alphabetical order.

_____

_____

_____

Vertical Challenge

7. (a) Write the answers to each clue in the correct place, horizontally on the grid.

- Scandalous (10)
- Taking part (13)
- Humiliate (9)
- Edition (5)
- Everlasting (9)
- Detailed examination (8)
- Proof (8)

(b) Write the word in the highlighted vertical column. _____

(c) Write a clue for this word. _____

_____

List Words	Practise	Practise	D
breathe			
humane			
morale			
clothe			
assassinate			
exaggerate			
assurance			
deterrent			
Ireland			
euro			

Incorrect Words

1. Write the list words correctly.

   (a) exagerate _____

   (b) deterrant _____

   (c) assassenate _____

   (d) assurence _____

   (e) breethe _____

   (f) ierland _____

Rhyming Words

2. Find a list or revision word that rhymes.

   (a) loathe _____

   (b) bureau _____

   (c) remain _____

   (d) seethe _____

   (e) blue _____

   (f) bought _____

Letters into Words

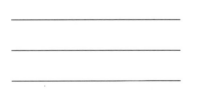

3. Write three list words using the letters on the map.

   _____

   _____

   _____

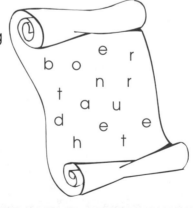

Revision Words

definite	adventure
astronaut	subdue
egotist	balcony

Difficult words I have found	Practise	Practise

4. Use list and revision words to solve this crossword.

Across

4. Overstate.
7. Murder.
8. It is meant to stop things happening.
11. Dress.

12. Self-esteem.
14. Escapade.
15. Veranda.

Down

1. Big headed person.
2. Inhale.
3. Certain.
5. Guarantee.
6. Placate.
7. Space traveller.
9. European currency.
10. The emerald isle.
13. Compassionate.

Mixed Up Sentences

6. Unjumble the sentences. Add a capital letter and a full stop.

(a) the not deterrent the do effectiveness exaggerate of

_____

(b) gave the safe the builder his that assurance was balcony

_____

Sentences

6. Write each of these words in a sentence.

(a) assassinate_____

_____

(b) egotist _____

_____

(c) deterrent _____

_____

List Words	Practise	Practise	D
ranger			
grocer			
manager			
officer			
collar			
similar			
regular			
peculiar			
byte			
multimedia			

Word Challenge

1. Make as many words as you can from letters in this word.

multimedia

_____

_____

_____

_____

_____

Small Words

2. Write the list word that contains these small words.

(a) time _____

(b) liar _____

(c) age _____

(d) ice _____

(e) ran _____

(f) man _____

Missing Letters

3. Complete these list words.

(a) __ i __ i __ __ __

(b) __ __ __ __ __ i __ __

(c) __ __ __ __ i __ __ __ i __

(d) __ __ __ i __ __ __

Revision Words

secretary	fury
calculator	puncture
award	rogue

Difficult words I have found	Practise	Practise

4. Find these list and revision words in the word search.

officer	regular
manager	similar
ranger	peculiar
grocer	collar
byte	multimedia
secretary	fury
calculator	puncture
award	rogue

t	o	f	f	i	c	e	r	r	e	w	y	q
y	b	v	c	p	e	c	u	l	i	a	r	r
r	n	c	t	y	r	u	i	o	p	e	a	a
a	a	r	o	i	u	a	y	t	g	l	t	n
l	m	i	o	l	s	d	l	a	r	k	e	g
u	m	r	d	a	l	v	n	i	e	j	r	e
g	r	o	c	e	r	a	c	f	m	h	c	r
e	n	g	p	z	m	x	r	g	w	i	e	u
r	b	u	l	a	k	i	j	h	q	g	s	t
u	v	e	e	w	w	e	t	y	b	f	x	c
i	r	o	t	a	l	u	c	l	a	c	z	n
o	c	x	z	r	a	s	d	f	u	r	y	u
p	l	k	j	d	h	g	f	d	s	m	a	p

Synonyms

5. Find a list or revision word with a similar meaning.

(a) even _____

(b) rascal _____

(c) strange _____

(d) alike _____

(e) rage _____

(f) boss _____

Secret Code

6. Use the secret code to find the list or revision word.

(a) __ __ __ __ __ __
    9 1 7 4 3 9

(b) __ __ __ __ __ __ __
    6 1 7 1 4 3 9

(c) __ __ __ __ __
    9 8 4 11 3

(d) __ __ __ __
    2 12 10 3

(e) __ __ __ __ __ __ __
    9 3 4 11 5 1 9

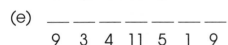

a	b	e	g	l	m	n	o	r	t	u	y
1	2	3	4	5	6	7	8	9	10	11	12

Word Worm Anagram

7. Circle the words written backwards in the word worm.
Rearrange the remaining letters to make a word.

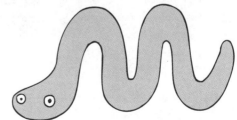

List Words	Practise	Practise	D
episode			
corrode			
implode			
explode			
aptitude			
latitude			
protrude			
attitude			
suddenly			
gone			

Mirror Writing

1. Write the mirror written words correctly.

    (a)   suddenly _____

    (b)   implode _____

    (c)   episode _____

    (d)   protrude _____

Verbs to Nouns

3. Complete the table.
You may use a dictionary.

       Verb   Noun

    (a)   explode   _____

    (b)   protrude   _____

    (c)   implode   _____

    (d)   corrode   _____

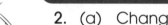

Secret Words

2. (a) Change 'sode' to 'logue' in episode.

      _____

    (b) Change 'lat' to 'long' in latitude.

      _____

    (c) Change 'rude' to 'ect' in protrude.

      _____

    (d) Change 'g' to 'al' in gone.

      _____

    (e) Change 'de' to 're' in explode.

      _____

Revision Words

optimism

raspberry

dormitory

escalator

contain

laundry

Difficult words I have found	Practise	Practise

4. Use list and revision words to solve this crossword.

Across

1. Moving stairway.
5. Include.
7. Leeway.
8. Occurrence.
9. Abruptly.
11. Large bedroom.
12. A small fruit.
13. Collapse violently.
14. Manner.

Down

1. Blow up.
2. Skill.
3. Past.
4. Stick out.
6. Hopefulness.
7. Washing.
10. Rust.

Missing Words

5. Use list or revision words to complete the sentences.

(a) The house master had to investigate the _____ in the

_____.

(b) The _____ trifle may _____ additives.

(c) His _____ is the reason for his positive _____.

(d) _____ your impatience, as the queue has almost

_____!

Memory Master

6. (a) Cover the list and revision words. Write three from memory.

_____   _____   _____

(b) For each word, write a question that has the word as its answer.

(i) _____

(ii) _____

(iii) _____

List Words	Practise	Practise	D
chimney			
curtsey			
chutney			
convey			
humour			
harbour			
armour			
neighbour			
being			
separate			

Alphabetical Order

1. Put the list and revision words with the pattern 'our' in alphabetical order.

   (a) _____

   (b) _____

   (c) _____

   (d) _____

   (e) _____

Changing Words

2. Change one letter in each word to make a list or revision word.

   (a) convoy _____

   (b) bring _____

   (c) tumour _____

   (d) mixture _____

   (e) treasure _____

   (f) tourism _____

Jumbled Words

3. Two list words are jumbled together. Write the two words.

   (a)   mostreaparerua

   _____ + _____

   (b)   haveboycorrun

   _____ + _____

Revision Words	
revolve	tourist
hurricane	treasury
environment	fixture

Difficult words I have found	Practise	Practise

4. Find these list and revision words in the word search.

chimney	armour
chutney	humour
convey	harbour
curtsey	neighbour
being	separate
revolve	tourist
hurricane	treasury
environment	fixture

y	e	n	m	i	h	c	h	u	t	n	e	y
q	x	n	z	a	r	m	o	u	r	a	s	d
c	o	n	v	e	y	y	u	i	f	o	p	f
w	g	t	j	i	k	l	p	r	i	o	y	g
e	n	a	c	i	r	r	u	h	x	i	r	h
e	i	r	h	c	r	o	x	z	t	u	u	e
r	e	e	g	v	b	u	n	a	u	y	s	v
t	b	w	f	h	s	f	o	m	r	t	a	l
y	c	q	g	b	n	m	b	b	e	r	e	o
t	s	i	r	u	o	t	d	s	r	n	r	v
u	e	q	w	e	s	e	p	a	r	a	t	e
n	v	b	n	m	l	r	u	o	m	u	h	r
c	u	r	t	s	e	y	i	o	p	l	k	j

My Meanings

5. Write a definition for each of these words. Use a dictionary to check your answers.

(a) hurricane _____

_____

_____

(b) curtsey _____

(c) environment _____

(d) fixture _____

(e) revolve _____

(f) convey _____

Word Worm Anagram

6. Find the four words that are written backwards and unjumble the remaining letters to make a fifth word.

List Words	Practise	Practise	D
you're			
couldn't			
they're			
doesn't			
violin			
violence			
violet			
ravioli			
during			
safety			

Incorrect Words

1. Write the list words correctly.

   (a) theyr'e _____

   (b) violance _____

   (c) couldent _____

   (d) voilet _____

   (e) your'e _____

   (f) dosen't _____

Rhyming Words

2. Find a list or revision word that rhymes.

   (a) hair _____

   (b) wouldn't _____

   (c) curing _____

   (d) pure _____

   (e) mandolin _____

   (f) mountain _____

   (g) silence _____

   (h) score _____

All Mixed Up

3. Unjumble the list words.

   (a) voirail _____

   (b) snoted _____

   (c) clovenie _____

   (d) nugrid _____

   (e) tfyesa _____

Revision Words

dinosaur	revenue
atheist	bulletin
sensory	fountain

Difficult words I have found	Practise	Practise

4. Use list and revision words to solve this crossword.

Across

1. An Italian dish.
3. A stringed instrument.
4. Does not.
10. Water spray.
11. You are.
12. Non-believer.
13. Income.
15. Could not.

Down

2. Speak.
4. Throughout.
5. To do with the senses.
6. They are.
7. Security.
8. An ancient extinct creature.
9. Press release.
14. The last rainbow colour.

Mixed Up Sentences

5. Unjumble the sentences. Add a capital letter and a full stop.

(a) officer display the the present during firework was safety

_____

(b) size in the he the dinosaur the believe of skeleton museum couldn't

_____

Sentences

6. Write each of these words in a sentence.

(a) doesn't _____

_____

(b) revenue _____

_____

(c) atheist _____

_____

List Words	Practise	Practise	D
opinion			
billion			
onion			
cushion			
dungeon			
surgeon			
galleon			
truncheon			
nervous			
advice			

Word Challenge

1. Make as many words as you can from letters in this word.

truncheon

_____

_____

_____

_____

Missing Letters

3. Complete these list words.

(a) __ __ __ __ c __ __ __ __ __

(b) __ p __ __ __ __ __ __

(c) __ __ r __ __ __ __ __

(d) __ a __ __ __ __ __

(e) __ i __ __ __ __ __

Small Words

2. Write the list word that contains these small words.

(a) ice _____

(b) urge _____

(c) all _____

(d) run _____

(e) in _____

(f) dung_____

(g) ill _____

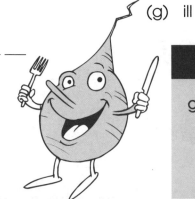

Revision Words	
government	thwart
petrol	criticism
blouse	laboratory

Difficult words I have found	Practise	Practise

4. Find these list and revision words in the word search.

opinion	dungeon
onion	galleon
cushion	surgeon
billion	truncheon
nervous	advice
government	thwart
petrol	criticism
blouse	laboratory

t	h	g	d	u	n	g	e	o	n	g	f	d
r	t	a	o	y	n	o	i	l	l	i	b	l
u	r	l	p	v	g	f	i	d	s	a	a	s
n	e	l	i	w	e	e	a	n	r	b	u	a
c	w	e	n	a	z	r	x	d	o	z	m	l
h	q	o	i	s	j	h	n	r	v	x	s	o
e	m	n	o	d	s	k	a	m	t	i	i	r
o	b	h	n	f	u	t	g	c	e	c	c	t
n	l	j	q	m	o	n	b	v	y	n	i	e
j	o	k	l	r	v	p	o	i	u	v	t	p
k	u	n	y	t	r	a	w	h	t	b	i	z
l	s	u	r	g	e	o	n	p	o	i	r	x
m	e	n	b	v	n	o	i	h	s	u	c	c

Secret Code

5. Use the secret code to find the list or revision word.

(a) __ __ __ __ __ __
2 8 10 14 12 4

(b) __ __ __ __ __ __ __
3 14 12 6 7 10 9

(c) __ __ __ __ __ __
13 6 15 1 11 13

(d) __ __ __ __ __
10 9 7 10 9

(e) __ __ __ __ __ __ __
12 14 11 5 4 10 9

(f) __ __ __ __ __ __ __
2 7 8 8 7 10 9

a	b	c	e	g	h	i	l	n	o	r	s	t	u	w
1	2	3	4	5	6	7	8	9	10	11	12	13	14	15

Extend Yourself

6. Use a dictionary to find the meaning of these two words. Write a sentence for each word.

(a) criticism _____

_____

(b) opinion _____

_____

(c) thwart _____

_____

List Words	Practise	Practise	D
courteous			
hideous			
courageous			
advantageous			
humorous			
delicious			
anxious			
vicious			
parallel			
resource			

Mirror Writing

1. Write the mirror written words correctly.

   (a) hideous _____

   (b) advantageous _____

   (c) courteous _____

   (d) vicious _____

   (e) anxious _____

Letters into Words

2. Write three list words using the letters on the parallelogram.

   _____

   _____

   _____

h	r	c	s	i	m	o	i
u	o	u	a	n	x	v	

Adjectives to Nouns

3. Complete the table.
   You may use a dictionary.

	Adjective	Noun
(a)	vicious	_____
(b)	anxious	_____
(c)	courageous	_____
(d)	humorous	_____

Revision Words

chateau	vegetable
restaurant	carol
pessimism	patio

Difficult words I have found	Practise	Practise

Unit 31

4. Use list and revision words to solve this crossword.

Across

1. Polite.
5. Negativity.
6. A Christmas hymn.
8. Of benefit.
10. Brave.
11. French country house.
13. Corresponding.
15. Amusing.

Down

2. A place to eat.
3. Brutal.
4. Scrumptious.
5. Terrace.
7. Supply.
9. A soup ingredient.
12. Ugly.
14. Worried.

Missing Words

5. Use list or revision words to complete the sentences.

(a) The _____ had been converted into a beautiful

_____.

(b) His _____ makes him very _____ about the future.

(c) It would be _____ to clean the _____ room after using it.

Memory Master

6. (a) Cover the list and revision words. Write three from memory.

_____ _____ _____

(b) For each word, write a question that has the word as its answer.

(i) _____

(ii) _____

(iii) _____

List Words	Practise	Practise	D
brackets			
width			
estimate			
analyse			
product			
negative			
perimeter			
diameter			
straight			
shoulder			

Jumbled Words

1. Two list words are jumbled together. Write the two words.

   (a)   thsadwigthirt

   _____ + _____

   (b)   oputheroddsurlc

   _____ + _____

Word Meanings

3. Match the words to their meanings.

   (a) product   *   * examine in detail

   (b) perimeter   *   * take the blame

   (c) analyse   *   * result of multiplying

   (d) shoulder   *   * outer edge

   (e) estimate   *   * measure of shortest side

   (f) width   *   * calculated guess

Secret Words

2. (a) Change 'est' to 'int' in estimate.

   _____

   (b) Change 'peri' to 'baro' in perimeter.

   _____

   (c) Change 'nega' to 'posi' in negative.

   _____

Revision Words	
cupboard	injury
gateau	solicitor
swarm	enrol

Difficult words I have found	Practise	Practise

4. Find these list and revision words in the word search.

brackets	width
estimate	analyse
product	negative
perimeter	diameter
straight	shoulder
cupboard	injury
gateau	solicitor
swarm	enrol

c	g	p	o	i	s	t	r	a	i	g	h	t
u	a	v	c	x	r	e	d	l	u	o	h	s
p	t	o	p	l	t	s	k	j	h	g	e	t
b	e	m	q	e	w	o	e	r	t	n	z	e
o	a	r	m	o	i	l	u	y	r	f	a	k
a	u	a	i	p	j	i	k	o	e	d	s	c
r	i	w	q	m	h	c	l	v	s	s	d	a
d	b	s	w	l	e	i	i	t	t	a	y	r
p	r	o	d	u	c	t	e	r	i	z	r	b
l	n	i	u	y	a	o	e	t	m	x	u	u
k	m	m	n	g	b	r	v	r	a	c	j	y
j	h	g	e	f	d	w	i	d	t	h	n	t
q	a	n	a	l	y	s	e	w	e	e	i	r

My Meanings

5. Write a definition for each of these words.
Use a dictionary to check your answers.

(a) swarm _____

(b) negative _____

(c) brackets _____

(d) enrol _____

(e) injury _____

(f) solicitor _____

(g) diameter _____

(h) straight _____

Word Worm Anagram

6. Find the four words that are written backwards and unjumble the remaining letters to make a fifth word.

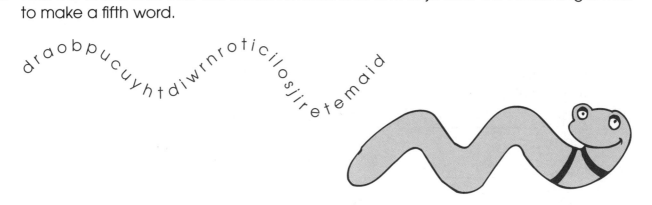

Revision Unit 5

List Words	Practise	Practise	D
parallel			
during			
multimedia			
resource			
separate			
straight			
safety			
shoulder			
nervous			
advice			

All Mixed Up

1. Unjumble these revision words.

   (a) t e a r p e a s   _____

   (b) m i d a t e m u l i   _____

   (c) c o r u s e e r   _____

   (d) d o e s h u r l   _____

   (e) l e a p r a l l   _____

   (f) g a s t h i r t   _____

   (g) e v r u n o s   _____

   (h) v e c i d a   _____

Shape Sorter

2. Write a word that fits in the shape.

   (a)

   (b)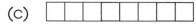

   (c)

Missing Words

3. Complete using the revision words.

   (a) The _____ strap over his _____ minimised his injuries.

   (b) I decided to take his _____ and go _____ to the police.

   (c) All the _____ equipment is kept in the _____ room.

   (d) I was very _____ _____ the performance on the _____ bars.

4. Find 12 mistakes and write them correctly on the lines.

A multimidia resourse reported the scoop about the circus scandal

_____

 dooring a performance on the paralell bars, the trapeze artist fell straigt

_____

through a faulty safty net, smashing his showlder.   seperate bulletin reports

_____

that a nervus ringmaster is seeking the advise of his solicitor.

_____

Word Hunt

5. (a) Which three words have only two vowels?   _____

_____   _____

(b) Which word has a prefix meaning 'many'?   _____

(c) Which two words can be verbs or nouns?   _____

Alphabetical Order

6. Write all the revision words in alphabetical order.

_____

_____

_____

Vertical Challenge

7. (a) Write the answers to each clue in the correct place, horizontally on the grid.

• Uneasy (7)

• Direct (8)

• Corresponding (8)

• Disks, TVs, graphics, etc. (10)

• A large joint in the body (8)

• Supply (8)

(b) Write the word in the highlighted vertical column. _____

(c) Write a clue for this word. _____

_____

My Dictionary Words: Aa to Ii _____

Aa	Bb	Cc

Dd	Ee	Ff

Gg	Hh	Ii

Jj	Kk	Ll
Mn	**Nn**	**Oo**
Pp	**Qq**	**Rr**

My Dictionary Words: Ss to Zz _____

Ss

Tt

Uu

Vv

Ww

Xx

Yy

Zz